Where Is the Cat?

Judy Nayer

Illustrated by Ann Boyajian

Rigby

The cat is not on the couch.

The cat is not on the bed.

The cat is not on the table.

The cat is not on the shelf.

The cat is not on the pillow.

The cat is not on the chair.

The cat is not on the desk.

The cat is not on me!